Little Scarlet's Big Fibs

Maverick
Early

'Little Scarlet's Big Fibs'
An original concept by Katie Dale
© Katie Dale

Illustrated by Kevin Payne

Published by MAVERICK ARTS PUBLISHING LTD
Studio 3A, City Business Centre, 6 Brighton Road,
Horsham, West Sussex, RH13 5BB
© Maverick Arts Publishing Limited August 2018
+44 (0)1403 256941

A CIP catalogue record for this book is available at the British Library.

ISBN 978-1-84886-370-5

Maverick
publishing
www.maverickbooks.co.uk

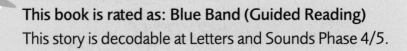

This book is rated as: Blue Band (Guided Reading)
This story is decodable at Letters and Sounds Phase 4/5.

Little Scarlet's Big Fibs

by **Katie Dale**
illustrated by **Kevin Payne**

"Take this bag of buns to Gran,"

said Scarlet's mum.

They smelled so good!

Scarlet just had to eat one.

5

Then another.

And another.

Oops! There are no buns left!

9

11

13

The next day, Mum handed Scarlet

a bag of tarts.

15

They smelled so good! Scarlet just
had to eat one.

16

Then another.

And another.

19

21

The next day, Mum handed Scarlet
a bag of muffins.

Take them to Gran. She likes banana muffins!

They smelled so good!

Scarlet just had to eat one.

But just then...

It was the Big Bad Wolf!

Scarlet ran off, dropping

the bag of muffins.

But it was **NOT** a wolf.

It was Gran!

Quiz

1. Which of these is Scarlet given take to Gran's?
a) Buns
b) A wolf
c) A car

2. How many buns does Scarlet eat?
a) Two
b) None
c) All of them

3. What does Scarlet tell Gran?
a) The Big Bad Wolf took them
b) She ate them
c) Birds took them

4. What flavour are the muffins?
a) Carrot
b) Banana
c) Apple

5. Who is the Big Bad Wolf?
a) Scarlet
b) Gran
c) Scarlet's mum

Turn over for answers

Book Bands for Guided Reading

The Institute of Education book banding system is a scale of colours that reflects the various levels of reading difficulty. The bands are assigned by taking into account the content, the language style, the layout and phonics.

Maverick Early Readers are a bright, attractive range of books covering the pink to purple bands. All of these books have been book banded for guided reading to the industry standard and edited by a leading educational consultant.

To view the whole Maverick Readers scheme, visit our website at

www.maverickearlyreaders.com

Or scan the QR code above to view our scheme instantly!

Quiz Answers: 1a, 2c, 3a, 4b, 5b